Razzamajazz

the fun way to learn!

Flute

Book 1

REVISED EDITION

Razzamajazz

the fun way to learn!

Flute

Book

1

SARAH
WATTS

kevin
mayhew

kevin mayhew

First published in Great Britain in 2001 by Kevin Mayhew Ltd
Buxhall, Stowmarket, Suffolk IP14 3BW
Tel: +44 (0) 1449 737978 Fax: +44 (0) 1449 737834
E-mail: info@kevinmayhewltd.com

www.kevinmayhew.com

9 8 7 6 5 4 3 2 1 0

ISBN 978 1 84003 719 7
ISMN M 57004 856 4
Catalogue No. 3611573

Cover design: Sara-Jane Came
Music setting: Donald Thomson
Proof reading: Marian Hellen

Printed and bound in Great Britain

Contents

B GROOVY

NOTE USED - B
CD Track 1

TWO AT TWILIGHT

NOTES USED - B, A
CD Track 2: Practice (♩ = 76)
CD Track 3: Performance (♩ = 98)

For and with Daniel Cashman

STRIPY CAT CRAWL

NOTES USED - B, A

CD Track 4: Practice (♩ = 100)

CD Track 5: Performance (♩ = 122)

JENCO'S JAM

NOTES USED - B, A, G

CD Track 6: Practice (♩ = 86)

CD Track 7: Performance (♩ = 116)

13
mp
mp
17
21
25

STARDOM WALTZ

NOTES USED - B, A, G

CD Track 8: Practice (♩ = 90)

CD Track 9: Performance (♩ = 112)

16
21
27
32
rall.
rall.
Ped.

Razzamajazz
The fun way to learn!

MR COOL

NOTES USED - B, A, G, C

CD Track 10: Practice (♩ = 100)

CD Track 11: Performance (♩ = 120)

Swing

mf

mf

6 *Optional vocals (spoken):*

Yeh! U-huh! Hit it!

11

That's cool Yeh!

16

U-huh! Hit it! I'm done!

SHRIMP CIRCUS

NOTES USED - B, A, G, C
CD Track 12: Practice (♩ = 86)
CD Track 13: Performance (♩ = 104)

10
(Spoken):
Two, three, four
p
p
14
Two, three, four
mf
mf
17
20

KIM'S BALLAD

NOTES USED - B, A, G, C
CD Track 14: Practice (♩ = 82)
CD Track 15: Performance (♩ = 96)

16
21
f
f
p
p
26
30
rall.
rall.
p

Razzamajazz

The fun way to learn!

UMBRELLA MAN

NOTES USED - A, G, C, D

CD Track 16: Practice (♩ = 86)

CD Track 17: Performance (♩ = 104)

MOVIE BUSTER

NOTES USED - B, A, G, C, D

CD Track 18: Practice (♩ = 84)

CD Track 19: Performance (♩ = 120)

21
mp
mp legato
26
f
f
31
35
ff
ff

MELLOW OUT

NOTES USED - B, A, G, C, D
CD Track 20: Practice (♩ = 66)
CD Track 21: Performance (♩ = 84)

17
21
25
29
p
rall.
p
rall.

HAIRY SCARY

NOTES USED - G, A, B, E

CD Track 22: Practice (♩ = 86)

CD Track 23: Performance (♩ = 108)

WATER LILIES

NOTES USED - G, A, B, C, D, E

CD Track 24: Practice (♩ = 72)

CD Track 25 Performance (♩ = 92)

Razzamajazz
The fun way to learn!

NOODLIN' AND DOODLIN'

NOTES USED - G, A, B, C, D, E
CD Track 26: Practice (♩ = 78)
CD Track 27: Performance (♩ = 110)

TEN TOE TAPPER

NOTES USED - G, A, B, C, D, E, low D

CD Track 28: Practice (♩ = 90)

CD Track 29: Performance (♩ = 116)

13
Tap dance! (or Woodblock solo)
mf
mf
18
22
26
p
p

PLAY OF LIGHT

NOTES USED - G, A, B, C, D, E, low D, F
CD Track 30: Practice (♩ = 90)
CD Track 31: Performance (♩ = 112)

13
mf
mf
17
22
p
p
27

SEA SPARKLE

NOTES USED - G, A, B, C, D, E, F

CD Track 32: Practice (♩ = 90)

CD Track 33: Performance (♩ = 112)

16
21
mp
mp
27
mf
mf
32
rall.
rall.

AND THEN EVENING CAME

NOTES USED - G, A, C, D, E, low D, F, B♭

CD Track 34: Practice (♩ = 78)

CD Track 35: Performance (♩ = 96)

13

17

MORNING IN MOSCOW

NOTES USED - G, A, C, E, low D, F, B♭

CD Track 36: Practice (♩ = 68)

CD Track 37: Performance (♩ = 80)

13

17
p
p

22
rall.
rall.

For Chris Hibberd

PEANUT BUTTER PALS

NOTES USED - G, A, B, C, D, E, low D, F, F♯

CD Track 38: Practice (♩ = 90)

CD Track 39: Performance (♩ = 112)

13

17
straight quavers
straight quavers

SHRIMP SHUFFLE

NOTES USED - G, A, B, C, D, E, low D, F, B♭, F♯

CD Track 40: Practice (♩ = 88)

CD Track 41: Performance (♩ = 106)

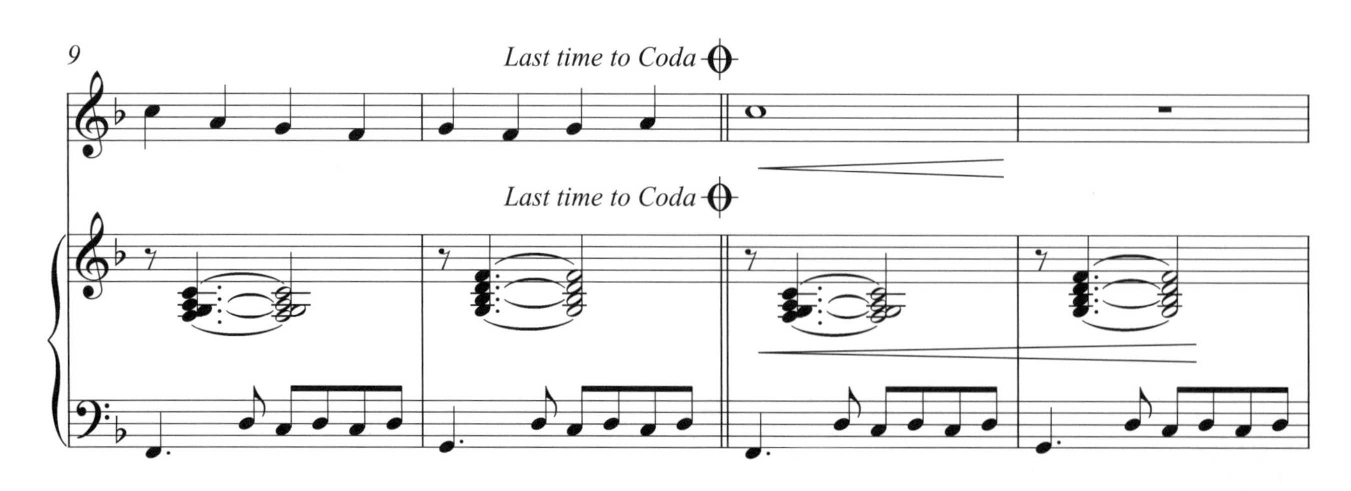

13
mf
mf

17

21
D.S. al Coda
p
D.S. al Coda
p

CODA
CODA
mf
mf
p
p
pp
pp

Razzamajazz

The fun way to learn!

BANANA TANGO

NOTES USED - G, A, B, C, D, E, F, F♯

CD Track 42: Practice (♩ = 80)

CD Track 43: Performance (♩ = 110)

13
Have a ba-na-na, have a ba-na-na, have a ba-na-na now.
f
f

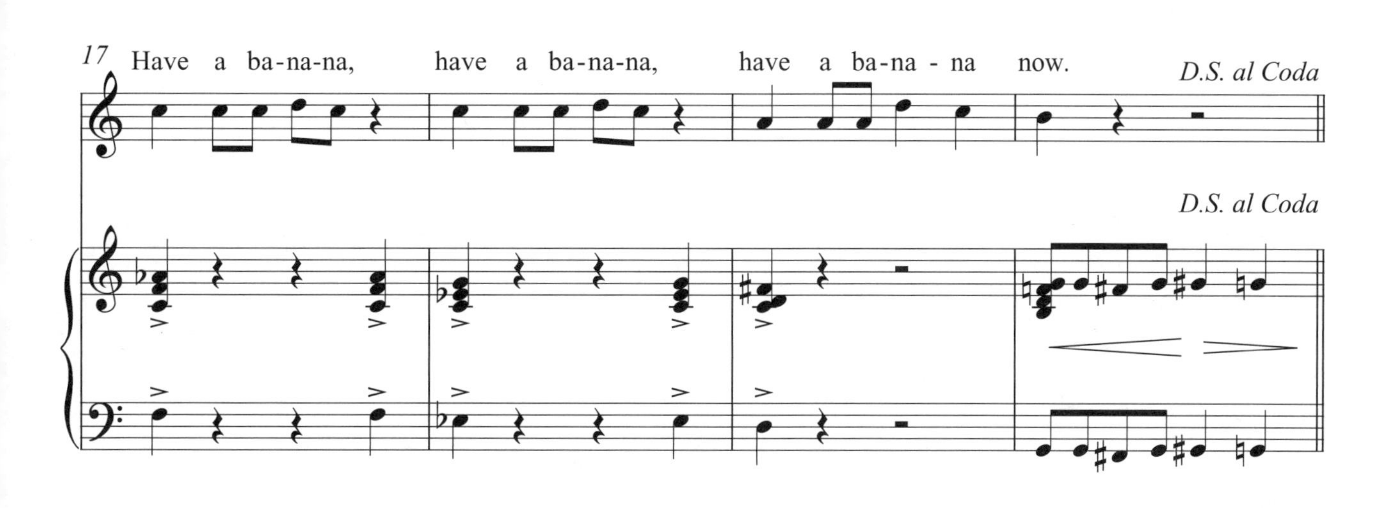
17
Have a ba-na-na, have a ba-na-na, have a ba-na - na now.
D.S. al Coda
D.S. al Coda

21
CODA
Have a ba-na - na now!
ff
CODA
ff
8vb